Biliju

and the planet Bilirose

Biliju

and the planet Bilirose

Written and illustrated by

Yseult Pierre

Originally translated by Sholom Wargon from
the French "Bilijou", Éditions Paulines, Montreal,
and Éditions Louis Musin, Paris, 1982.

biliju.net

PAPERBACK: 978-1-950256-40-2
EBOOK: 978-1-950256-41-9

Ordering Information:

For orders and inquiries, please contact:
1-888-375-9818
www.toplinkpublishing.com
bookorder@toplinkpublishing.com

Printed in the United States of America

In the sky, there are planets of every colour...
And one is grey.

On this planet, everything is grey. The houses and trees are grey. The fields and meadows are grey. Here, life is dull and monotonous. Even in good weather, the sky is grey.

One morning, Nicholas goes out for a walk. The sun is warm and the grass in the fields sways in the soft breeze.

Nicholas absent-mindedly watches the flowers and the grass as they dance in the breeze, then stops to listen to the wind whispering.

He is fascinated by this little world of grass, leaves and flowers. Everything seems to be swaying to a music sung by the wind.

Captivated by their dance, Nicholas begins to move with them. Soon, all are dancing as one.

Suddenly, the grass, the daisies, the poppies change
before his eyes. The meadow becomes radiant, vibrant,
more alive than before.

6

Nicholas can't believe his eyes. He closes them, then opens them again. The distant hills are as dull as ever. But the meadow under his feet is strangely vivid. And what is this, he wonders? A new flower? No - it's a tiny creature! Wait - it's growing! Bigger - and bigger and bigger! Soon it is as big as Nicholas.

"Hello! My name is Zeb. I am a Biliju. What is your name?
   - I'm Nicholas. I don't understand... What's happening?
   - Colour! Colour changes everything! If you want to learn more, just come with me to my planet, Bilirose."

   Nicholas is amazed, but he is not afraid. He takes the Biliju's hand. Zeb says:
   "Now, think about your dreams. That will make you lighter."

Nicholas suddenly finds himself in a thick pink fog.
Soon the fog clears and Nicholas sees a planet
- the planet Bilirose.

Nicholas is delighted! Colour - colour everywhere, as far as he can see.

"Look, Nicholas," says the Biliju. "This peaceful flower is *blue*, this flaming butterfly is *red*, this joyful blossom is *yellow*."

But Nicholas' excitement fades. He sighs. "It's so colourful here. Why is my planet all grey?"

11

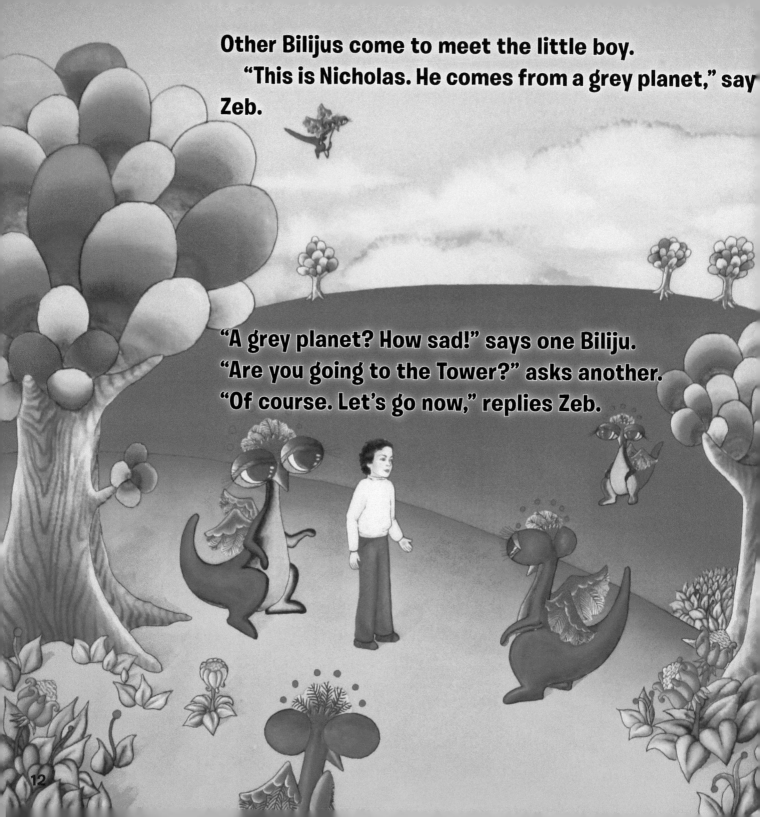

Other Bilijus come to meet the little boy.

"This is Nicholas. He comes from a grey planet," say Zeb.

"A grey planet? How sad!" says one Biliju.
"Are you going to the Tower?" asks another.
"Of course. Let's go now," replies Zeb.

The Bilijus lead Nicholas to a tall sparkling tower.
"In the Tower, you will find out what happened to your planet," says
Zeb. "The Keeper of the Tower will escort you."
Zeb knocks on the door. The Keeper appears.

"Hello Nicholas, I am Zir, the Keeper of the Tower. Come with me and all your questions will be answered. The Tower knows all, shows all."

"Knows all, shows all?" murmurs Nicholas. "Wow!"

Nicholas follows Zir into the strange and wonderful Tower. Inside, a round platform glows softly. Zir invites Nicholas to sit.

"Watch closely and you'll see why your planet is grey," whispers Zir.

16

A cloud forms in the center of the room. And in it Nicholas sees his planet take shape. But everything is in colour! It's so much prettier. And it's so joyful, thinks Nicholas. But even as these thoughts enter his head, he sees something troubling.

It's the people. They don't notice the breeze. They don't appreciate the flowers. Nature feels sad, neglected. Soon her beautiful colours fade. Nicholas understands her sorrow. Nobody cares about her. Finally, everything becomes grey...

But then another vision emerges. In the middle of all that grey, he sees a boy dancing in a green meadow.

"You see, Nicholas? When you danced in the wind, you gave the grass and flowers back their colour!" says Zir.

Nicholas jumps up. "I know how to save my planet!" he says. "I'll get my friends and we'll dance in the fields to show Nature we care!"

When Nicholas leaves the Tower, the other Bilijus are waiting for him.

"Your planet and your people need you," says Zir.

Nicholas says goodbye to the Bilijus, takes Zeb's hand and...

...finds himself back in the green meadow, in the middle of the grey planet.

"Goodbye Nicholas" says Zeb. "Good luck!" And he is gone.

Nicholas brings his friends to see the little green meadow. The children are entranced by the bright green grass and the sparkling flowers. Nicholas tells them how sad Nature is when people ignore her. The children discover how beautiful the flowers are, how soft the wind, and how magnificent the mountains.

Nicholas and his friends run to the city to tell everyone about the beauty and wonder of Nature.

For the first time in a very long time, their hearts are filled with joy.

The entire planet comes alive with colour. A glorious rainbow appears.

In the sky, there are planets of every colour...
And *none* of them are grey!

Just add colour

CPSIA information can be obtained
at www.ICGtesting.com
Printed in the USA
BVHW022005130219
540209BV00001B/3/P